Alfred Nobel

by Tore Frängsmyr

SVENSKA INSTITUTET

Stockholm

CONTENTS

© 1996 Tore Frängsmyr and the Swedish Institute (SI)

The author alone is responsible for the views expressed in this publication.

Translation by Judith Black

Graphic design by Anders Rahm

Cover photo: Alfred Nobel aged about 50. © The Nobel Foundation

Printed in Sweden by BTJ Tryck AB, Lund 1996

ISBN 91-520-0417-1

ISSN 1101-6353

NO SWEDE, not even the sporting or pop stars of our own age, can be better known to the world at large than Alfred Nobel. Nevertheless, even this widespread fame has to be described as more indirect than direct. In other words, the Nobel Prizes are extremely well-known everywhere, while the person behind them remains relatively unknown.

A fair amount has, admittedly, been written about Alfred Nobel, but much of it is stereotypical—portraits of the lonely millionaire, unhappy or at least deeply melancholy in spite of his wealth, emotionally attached to his mother and scarred by one or two traumatic amorous entanglements. This is not wholly incorrect. Alfred Nobel was lonely and he was clearly unhappy in his love life, but descriptions of this kind do not get us very far. The romance is a separate literary genre and I do not intend to contribute to it here. I shall, rather, attempt to present a more general picture of the man himself and his scientific and technical achievements.

To start with, a number of important biographical facts. Alfred Nobel was born in 1833, the son of an engineer. His family background is interesting, however, because one of Alfred's ancestors was none other than Olof Rudbeck the Elder, the foremost technical genius of Sweden's great power era. Rudbeck (1630–1702) personified Swedish culture at the time when the country's empire was at its zenith. As professor of medicine at Uppsala University he made tremendous achievements not only in the fields of medicine (he discovered the human lymphatic system), but also as a botanist, historian, composer, architect and engineer. He built houses and bridges, constructed aqueducts and lock systems, laid out botanical gardens and organized training in the arts of gunnery and fortification. One is tempted to believe that there might have been a link between Alfred Nobel's technical aptitude and Rudbeck's brilliant and versatile talents.

Rudbeck's daughter Wendela married one Petrus Nobelius, whose name was the latinized version of his birthplace, Nöbbelöv in Skåne, southern Sweden. The family name was then shortened to Nobel by his grandson Immanuel, Alfred Nobel's grandfather. The latter's son (Alfred's father), was also called Immanuel. He had received a technical education and worked as an architect and building contractor. His career got off to a brilliant start but soon suffered setbacks, and in 1833, the year of Alfred's birth, he went bankrupt. It was ten years before Immanuel Nobel was completely free of his creditors, but he never gave up; he was constantly embarking on new technical projects.

When Alfred was five his father moved to St. Petersburg, where he set up an engineering workshop to manufacture anti-personnel mines for the Russian army. Alfred's mother, Andriette, had to remain in Stockholm and provide for her sons. She had a small milk and vegetable shop which helped them to survive. The story goes that Alfred and his two brothers, Robert and Ludvig, had to earn their keep by selling matches. (The fourth son, Emil, was born later.)

Adolescence and Education

In 1842, when Alfred was nine years old, the family moved to St. Petersburg. The father's fortunes had turned and the family was now able to enjoy a life typical of the bourgeoisie of the time. St. Petersburg was a great European metropolis, rich with culture and science and sparkling society. The Nobel boys were instructed by leading university professors rather than going to school. Their education embraced both the humanities and the natural sciences. In addition to Swedish, Alfred and his brothers were taught Russian, French, English and German, as well as

The Nobel family home in St. Petersburg. Photo: © The Nobel Foundation.

literature and philosophy. In the natural sciences their education
was guided by two professors of chemistry, Yuli Trapp and
Nicolai Zinin, who taught them mathematics, physics and
chemistry. It was perhaps no coincidence, given the specialist
field of these teachers, that Alfred was attracted to chemistry. He
learnt to carry out chemical experiments, an activity which
seems to have fascinated him right from the start.

Alfred was to spend his most important formative years in the
then Russian capital, and with all his five languages, which he
appears to have commanded well, he lay the foundations of the
cosmopolitanism which was to be so characteristic of him in
later life.

In the period 1850 to 1852, Alfred undertook a number of
trips abroad for study purposes. He spent one year in Paris with
the famous chemist Jules Pelouze, who was a professor at the
Collège de France, but who at that time had just opened a

private teaching laboratory. Pelouze, who was incidentally a good friend of the great Swedish chemist Berzelius (1779–1848), had also been the teacher of Alfred Nobel's private tutor Nicolai Zinin. It was during this year in Paris that Alfred completed his training as a chemist. It is also to this period that we can trace the roots of what was to be his life's greatest discovery. For it was here, if not before, that he must have heard about the remarkable explosive, nitroglycerine. Strangely enough, this has never been taken up by Nobel researchers, who tend to identify the important moment as coming ten years later.

The background was as follows: in 1847 in Turin, an Italian pupil of Pelouze, Ascanio Sobrero, had discovered a new explosive which he initially called pyroglycerine (later nitroglycerine). However, in letters to Pelouze as well as in a later scientific paper, Sobrero sounded a warning about the new substance: not only did it possess a formidable explosive power but it was also impossible to control. Sobrero's discovery did not come out of the blue. The way had already been paved in the 1830s by Pelouze himself, among others, when he had worked on the production of gun-cotton. Since Alfred Nobel was greatly interested in explosives—they were, after all, 'in the family'— and since Pelouze had first-hand knowledge of producing explosives, Alfred must already have learnt of nitroglycerine. However, the excitement of the discovery was immediately dampened by the difficulty in producing and handling the new substance.

The Inventor

THE END of the Crimean War in 1856 spelled disaster for the Nobel factory, whose survival depended on the demand for war munitions. The factory went into liquidation and the parents moved home to Sweden. Their three sons remained in St. Petersburg to sort out affairs and reconstruct the company. At this point, Alfred and his brothers discussed a number of possible projects with their former tutors, and it was now that Nicolai Zinin reminded them of the potential of nitroglycerine. He is said to have demonstrated its power by pouring a few drops onto an anvil, hitting it with a hammer and causing a sharp explosion. But only that part of the liquid which came into contact with the hammer exploded. The problems, which Sobrero had already understood, were twofold. Firstly, the substance was difficult to produce, since it exploded if the temperature rose too high. Secondly, even if one succeeded in producing a small amount, the next problem was getting it to explode under controlled conditions.

In the years around 1860, Alfred carried out repeated experiments at great risk. His first achievement was in producing nitroglycerine in sufficient amounts with no mishaps. He then mixed the nitroglycerine with black powder and ignited the mixture with an ordinary fuse. After a number of successful trials on a stretch of the frozen River Neva outside St. Petersburg, Alfred travelled back to Stockholm, where his father had begun similar experiments (although with less success), after hearing of Alfred's activities by letter. The father even tried to assert that the new design was his own, but after a sharp letter from Alfred setting things straight, he changed his mind and helped instead with the patent application which Alfred submitted in his own name. In 1863 a patent was granted for the explosive, which Alfred appropriately called "blasting oil".

With this first patent the first milestone was also reached. Alfred was only thirty years old, but his invention marked the beginning of a thrilling adventure which was to unfold with astonishing speed. During the following spring and summer, Alfred continued his experiments. He was soon ready with a new patent, this time for the production of nitroglycerine (by a simpler method) and the use of a detonator, or "Nobel Igniter" as it was called—a hollow wooden plug which was filled with

Alfred Nobel aged about 30. Photo: © The Nobel Foundation.

black powder, later called a "percussion cap" or detonator. The design was very soon improved by replacing the wooden plug with a metal cap. The invention proved revolutionary in the field of explosives, for it was only now that the explosive potential of nitroglycerine could be exploited effectively.

Many have since argued that the percussion cap was in fact a more important invention than was dynamite itself. It has been called the greatest advance in the field of explosives since the introduction of black powder to the West in the 15th century. Ragnar Sohlman, Nobel's closest associate during his last years, was one of those who felt that the percussion cap, as a technical construction, should be ranked ahead of dynamite. Others have described it as the greatest discovery ever made in both the theory and practice of explosives. And Nobel himself seems to have shared this view, saying, ten years later, that the "real nitroglycerine age" had begun with his invention in 1864.

It is thus apparent that the determination and self-confidence which were to become ever more apparent in Alfred were already in place at this early stage of his career. He himself wrote that he was "the first person to move these substances out of the science laboratory and into the world of industry". He now succeeded in securing a sizeable loan from a French bank.

The Entrepreneur

IT WAS now that the next trait of his personality revealed itself: the inventor joined forces with the entrepreneur. Successes and setbacks were met with the same spirit of resolve. September 1864 witnessed the great explosion at the factory outside Stockholm in which Alfred's brother Emil and four others lost their lives. This was obviously a catastrophe. The deaths were a tragedy in themselves; to this can be added the public fears and the rumour-mongering to which the accident gave rise. Alfred's father suffered a stroke shortly after, but Alfred himself stood firm; he knew what he wanted and he intended to carry out his plans in spite of the tragic accident. A mere month later he established his first limited company, single-mindedly and without sentiment. He had difficulty in obtaining permission to set up a new factory; the police decided that it had to be located outside the town because of the risk of further explosions. So the manufacture of blasting oil started on a barge on Lake Mälaren, Stockholm. Nobel subsequently purchased a stable in Vinterviken, just south of the then city boundary, where a laboratory and factory were built.

Serious production could now get under way. The new company met with an encouraging response on the markets. A large number of shares had been purchased by J.W. Smitt, the wealthy businessman who had made his fortune in South Africa. Orders started to stream in, in spite of, or maybe even because of, the accident—for there could be no doubt about the explosive force of the new substance. The Swedish state railways, for example, ordered blasting oil for their work on the Söder (southern) railway tunnel in Stockholm. The following year, in 1865, Alfred completed his improved version of the metal percussion cap, essentially the same design as that of today's detonators.

After this, the rest of the world beckoned. Nobel travelled round in a number of countries, sounding out the field. He obtained patents for his blasting oil in Britain, Norway and Finland and embarked on negotiations with several other countries. Everything went with great speed. In March 1865, Nobel set off for Hamburg; three months later he set up his first company outside Sweden, in Hamburg, with the brothers Wilhelm and Theodor Winkler and the business lawyer C.E. Bandmann. In the autumn of the same year, they acquired land in a valley in Krümmel an der Elbe, just south of Hamburg, where a factory was built. At New Year 1866, Alfred demonstrated the explosive in a quarry in north Wales, but little interest was shown in Britain. A few months later he was en

The barge, anchored in Lake Mälaren, Stockholm, upon which the first commercial production of nitroglycerine took place in the winter of 1864/65. Photo: © The Nobel Foundation.

route for America, where he arrived in mid-April.

The atmosphere in America was tense. A number of serious explosions had occurred in quick succession in the USA, Europe and Australia, and in each case the cause was said to be crates of nitroglycerine. In all, several hundred people had lost their lives. In some cases the crates had been sent from Nobel's factories in Europe. The public was highly alarmed and Congress was just then considering a total ban on the transportation of the dangerous substance. Such a ban would, of course, have made it impossible for Nobel to develop his industry and sell his products.

The press portrayed Nobel as a dangerous man, and he therefore decided to take the bull by the horns. He asked the mayor of New York to allow him to demonstrate his method of handling nitroglycerine, in the form of his blasting oil. In May 1866, these trial explosions took place in a quarry in Upper Manhattan, an area which at that time had not yet been developed. The explosions went according to plan and, moreover, under the strict personal supervision of Nobel himself. This impressed the spectators and the general public, and undoubtedly helped, together with a deal of lobbying, substantially to tone down Congress's ban. The only requirement now was for warning labels to be affixed to the dangerous transportations. The day after the congressional decision, Nobel and his American partners established the "United States Blasting Oil Company".

Dynamite

IN SPITE of the slow communications of the age, everything now proceeded quickly; events followed upon each other in rapid succession. The factory in Germany blew up during Alfred's stay in America. Upon his return there in August he had to clear up and start planning his new premises.

For the time being, though, Nobel was once again obliged to set up his laboratory on a barge, this time moored on the River Elbe near the ruins of his factory. There was not a moment to lose. It was clear that the blasting oil, in spite of everything, was not stable and that transportation or lengthy storage was highly risky. So Nobel pondered over the problem of safety, all the time carrying out new experiments. He realized that the nitroglycerine had to be absorbed by some porous material and mixed with another substance if it were to be rendered safer to handle. He systematically tested a whole range of additives, such as charcoal, sawdust and cement, but without success.

In the end, Nobel came upon what he was searching for almost by chance. On the German heathlands, just where he

Nobel monument 'Blown up Tree' on the bank of the River Neva, St. Petersburg, Russia. Photo: Susanne Concha Emmrich.

happened to be based, he discovered a porous and absorbent sand called kiselguhr, known locally on the Lüneburger Heide as heidberg sand. When the kiselguhr soaked up the nitroglycerine it formed a paste or kneadable mass. This paste could be made into sticks, which could then easily be inserted into the drill hole and exposed to the knocks and jolts of transportation without exploding. It could even be ignited without anything happening, for it was the percussion cap which caused the paste to explode. The disadvantage of the new substance was that the explosive power of the nitroglycerine was somewhat reduced, since the kiselguhr was not an active substance, but it was the price that had to be paid.

This, in brief, was how dynamite was invented. The name,

incidentally, was chosen by Nobel after the Greek word for "power". His German colleagues had suggested the term "blasting putty", but Alfred thought it sounded as if it were intended for blasting window panes, which was not at all the case. In the course of 1867 he obtained patents for dynamite in several countries, most importantly Britain, Sweden and the USA. Large-scale production could get under way; demand grew rapidly. Grand construction projects such as railways, harbours, bridges, mines and not least tunnels, all of which necessitated blasting, were a feature of the age. In the construction of the Sankt Gotthard tunnel through the Alps in the 1870s, for example, dynamite was of crucial importance.

In 1868, the year after the patent, Alfred Nobel and his father were awarded the Letterstedtska Prize by the Royal Swedish Academy of Sciences, a prize which Alfred coveted highly. It was given for "important discoveries of practical value for mankind". An echo of this formulation can be heard in the wording of Nobel's own prizes.

The most decisive stretch of Alfred Nobel's path to fame and glory had now been covered. Let us pause a while in the year 1873. Alfred was now forty years of age. Everything had happened in the preceding ten years. He had obtained his first patent at the age of thirty. Now at the age of forty he had already made his most important discoveries, built up a global empire, made his fortune and bought a large house in the heart of Paris. The foundations were laid. He went on to make new discoveries, most notably gelignite and ballistite, and his company grew, as did his wealth. His most characteristic feature was his versatility. He was inventor, industrial magnate and organizer. He had to protect his patents, develop his products, set up new companies and correspond with all the corners of the globe in five languages, all without secretarial assistance and before the telephone and telefax had bestowed their blessings on

mankind; he was constantly out travelling by train and boat

before the days of aviation; factories blew up; scaremongering was rife; companies were revealed to be fraudulent. All of this he had to deal with single-handedly. Moreover, he was seldom really well; he felt ill and frail, complained frequently of migraine, rheumatism and a poor stomach. Life was one mad rush, "sheer torture", in his own words. People are mad, he wrote in letters from Paris; they rushed in and out of his office; everyone wanted to meet him and they expected him to be everywhere at once. But he coped, in spite of everything; in the role of entrepreneur he was unbeatable.

Restlessness was of course an important ingredient of his inventive genius. He could not be content with his successes; he was constantly trying to improve his designs. Not even dynamite was perfect; he thought its explosive power too weak, so in 1875 he made an improved version, or a new discovery if you like, in the shape of gelignite. The story behind this reveals his curiosity and the way he worked. It took place in Paris.

According to his own account, he had cut his finger and gone down to his laboratory in the night to brush some collodion onto his finger. This formed an elastic film over the wound. He started to muse on the substance and suddenly came upon the idea of mixing nitroglycerine into a bowl containing collodion. The nitroglycerine immediately dissolved and the result was a jelly-like mass, the consistency of which could be varied according to the proportions used. He continued his experimentation all night, and when his colleagues arrived next morning he was able to present his new invention, gelignite, which not only had a stronger explosive effect than pure nitroglycerine but was also chemically stable and insensitive to impact.

A few years later, Nobel invented a smokeless powder, which he called ballistite but is usually called Nobel gunpowder. It came to replace the black powder which gave off the "gunsmoke" so characteristic of gunfights. By combining nitrocellulose and nitroglycerine Nobel obtained a powder which pro-

The company's tug which pulled barges loaded with raw materials and dynamite. In the background, the Nobel factory (1880s). Photo: Nitro Nobel AB.

duced water vapour rather than smoke. A laboratory to develop his new invention was set up in 1881 in Sévran-Livry outside Paris, but it was not until 1887 that he succeeded in obtaining his first patent on the substance, this too in France.

Nobel worked on many other projects simultaneously. Whether it be synthetic rubber or leather, aluminium boats, aeroplane designs or domestic refrigerators, his creative drive never rested. He himself wrote at one point: "If I have 300 ideas in a year and one of them is useable, then I'm satisfied."

The Leader of Industry

THE ABILITIES to organize and to maintain a clear perspective, as well as an awareness of the march of time, can be identified as some of the driving features behind Alfred Nobel's success as a leader of industry. The last-mentioned was perhaps more important than might initially seem to be the case.

Nobel seems always to have felt pressed for time. A number of his inventions were already to some extent in the offing— because the times were crying out for them. His patents were always a little shaky, some could be exploited illegally. Some of his business partners were less than particular, sometimes outright criminal. Politicians and bureaucrats did nothing to make life easy for an inventor of explosives. The general public was easily alarmed and moulded opinion. And in some cases, self-interest, even as high up as in government circles, was at work against Nobel's companies.

Nobel's strategy was to get onto a market as quickly as possible and then build factories for large-scale production, in order to preempt or neutralize any possible competitors. The first dynamite factory in the USA was built as early as the autumn of 1867 at Rock House Canyon outside San Francisco. Demand then proved so great that it had to be expanded within two years. Nobel had obtained a British patent as early as the spring of 1867, yet problems arose, despite successful demonstrations in Surrey in the summer of the same year. Not until 1871, after a whole series of political and legal complications, could the "British Dynamite Company" be established. But by then Nobel had tired of the English and he consequently set up his factory in Scotland (1872), at Ardeer on the west coast. The company's managing director was his faithful partner John Downie, but Nobel himself took an active part in building it up. As always, he installed a private laboratory for himself, and he bought a house in the village of Lauriston, where he spent long periods in the 1870s.

Nobel also encountered initial difficulties in France. There was originally a ban on the production of dynamite, but the French changed their tune with the outbreak of the Franco-Prussian War of 1870–71. In 1871, in record-quick time, a factory was built in Paulille, southern France, in collaboration with Nobel's French partner, the engineer and former artillery officer Paul Barbe. However, the riots of the Paris Commune followed in the late spring, and the liberal use of explosives there alarmed the politicians anew. All private production of dynamite and similar substances was accordingly banned in France that autumn. Nobel and Barbe were not the only protesters at this; they were supported by mine-owners, tunnel constructors and railway companies. After heavy lobbying and much political wrangling, the ban was lifted again in March 1875.

The pace was fevered. In the period 1871–73 Nobel set up ten factories in nine countries—17 in all by 1873. Apart from those already mentioned, factories were set up in Austria, Spain, Switzerland, Italy and Portugal.

All of this naturally rendered the need to maintain a clear overview and to encourage cooperation between companies vital, and this was what Nobel worked hard at in the years 1875 to 1883. Firstly, he merged all the factories in each country to form parent companies. He then brought together all the latter into trust companies, or concerns as we would call them today. Shortly before, John D. Rockefeller had amalgamated all his oil interests to form the world's first trust, "The Standard Oil Co.".

Nobel's first trust comprised the British and German companies and was called "The Nobel Dynamite Trust Company Ltd", with headquarters in London and a share capital of two million pounds. A second trust, the "Société Centrale de Dynamite", was constructed for southern Europe, with headquarters in Paris and a share capital of 16 million francs. It comprised the French, Italian, Swiss, Spanish and Portuguese companies. At the time of Nobel's death in 1896 there were Nobel parent companies in some 20 countries, while explosives of all kinds were being manufactured under his patents in hundreds of factories throughout the whole world.

In addition to all this, Alfred Nobel also took part in the

Visit of Tsar Alexander III to the Nobel brothers' naphtha (petroleum) company in Baku 1888. Photo: County Archive, Lund

business activities of his brothers, Robert and Ludvig, in Russia. After their father's bankruptcy they had salvaged the business and set up a successful engineering workshop in St. Petersburg. They subsequently turned their attention to oil and built up the great network of oilfields in Baku, Azerbaidzhan. Among other things they built the world's first oil tanker. Alfred joined the oil company as a partner and financial guarantor; his brother Ludvig was responsible for imports of dynamite to Russia. The collaboration between the brothers was good and fruitful.

The Humanist

THERE WAS another side to Alfred Nobel's character which should rightly be touched upon here, namely the humanist and the philosopher. We know that he had literary interests and ambitions; he read a great deal of fiction and wrote dramas and poetry. Although it might surprise us, his favourite poet was Shelley—this atheist and revolutionary harboured a sensitive poetic soul.

Nobel also demonstrated an interest in philosophical matters. Among the papers he left is a black notebook of philosophy, hitherto overlooked by his biographers. The notebook contains no great original thoughts, but these pencil notes do nevertheless demonstrate a serious interest in philosophical issues. Nobel went through the development of philosophy from classical times to his own day and indicated what he believed to be important questions. He wrote his own commentaries, the somewhat sceptical tone of which indicates that he maintained a distance from his subject. He gave his views of Plato, Aristotle and Democritus, as well as Newton and Voltaire and contemporary biologists such as Darwin and Haeckel. He wrote, for example, that it is unclear what it was that caused Man to come upon the idea of a God: "Aristotle attributes it to fear, Voltaire to the desire of the clever to fool the stupid." He wrote with respect of the philosophical doubts of Descartes and Spinoza, feeling that this must rightly constitute the starting point for all philosophizing. He was particularly interested in matters of knowledge. He returned several times to Locke's thesis about all knowledge emanating from sensory impressions, and maintained, accordingly, that "the brain is a register of impressions of a highly unstable nature."

This led him on to reflect upon the working methods of science, and he developed a train of thought which seems to have been inspired not only by Locke but also by Alexander von Humboldt. All science is based on the observation of similarity and dissimilarity, wrote Nobel, and continued:

"For a chemical analysis is nothing else and mathematics itself has no other basis. History is a picture of past similarities and dissimilarities; geography demonstrates the dissimilarities of the earth's surface, geology the similarities and dissimilarities in the earth's formation, from which we may deduce the course of its transformations. Astronomy is a study of the similarities and dissimilarities in the heavenly bodies; physics is the study of the similarities and dissimilarities which arise through the attraction and movements of matter. The only exception to this rule is theology, although even this relies on the similarity in gullibility common to so many. Even metaphysics, if it is not excessively crazy, has to support its hypotheses on some kind of analogy. One may without exaggeration claim that what lies at the heart of all human knowledge is the observation of and the search for similarities and dissimilarities."

Nobel could have concluded his train of thought with Humboldt's words that "from observation one proceeds to experimentation ... based on analogies and the induction of empirical laws". This was no grand theory of knowledge but rather an empirical method. Alfred Nobel surely felt that he had got quite far by applying this method in his work.

Perhaps even more interesting are Nobel's thoughts concerning war and peace. It is often said that he established a peace prize because he had a bad conscience about his weapons industry. This cannot have been the case, for a start, because of the fact that his explosives, with the exception of ballistite, were not used in war during his lifetime. In his contacts with Bertha von Suttner (see page 23) he often discussed peace issues and defended himself against criticism of his own activities. It could well be that my factories, he said on one occasion, will put an end to war more quickly than your peace conferences, for when two armies of equal strength can annihilate each other in an instant, then all civilized nations will retreat and disband their troops.

Nobel often returned to this viewpoint. We may well feel that it indicates a naive attitude on Nobel's part, yet the same argument is still used in our own day. Bertha von Suttner tried to engage Nobel personally in her work for peace. He became a member of the Austrian peace union and he donated money to the cause, but he ultimately felt that the peace movement lacked a realistic programme. He himself favoured the idea of establishing a court of arbitration to deal with international disputes; for a twelve-month period, while negotiations were under way, the parties would be prohibited from using force. For a few years Nobel even employed a Turkish diplomat, Aristarchi Bey, to keep him informed about and assist him in peace issues.

Given all this, it was only natural that efforts to promote peace should be recognized in Nobel's will. The prize was to go to "the person who shall have done the most or the best work for fraternity between nations, for the abolition of standing armies and for the holding and formation of peace congresses".

The Private Man

As an individual, Alfred Nobel remained fairly anonymous. He was reticent and somewhat shy. He disliked mixing in large company and often declined invitations to official banquets. He was in truth an unassuming man who had no wish to keep court or indulge in extravagance.

In addition to this, of course, a person in Nobel's position was always a figure of public interest. Opportunists jostled to meet him, the press watched him, the general public was periodically outraged by his activities. It was not so strange that he became sceptical and wanted to keep his fellow man at arm's length.

The sensitivity of Nobel's nature is evident in many ways, such as in the story about Sobrero. As we have already seen, the latter was undeniably the discoverer of nitroglycerine, but he had also claimed that the substance could not be employed or developed because of its dangerous nature. However, when Nobel had managed to tame its powers and make a fortune from it, Sobrero woke up. In an article in a journal in 1870, Sobrero claimed that his discovery had been unjustly forgotten and he demanded acknowledgement for his contribution. Even though Nobel and his contemporaries clearly recognized the dividing line between Sobrero's discovery and Nobel's application thereof, Nobel certainly took Sobrero's indignation to heart. He engaged the latter as a consultant in his Swiss-Italian company and paid him a generous retaining fee. After Sobrero's death in 1888, a statue of him was erected at the factory in Avigliana and his widow continued to receive payment for the rest of her life.

Neither could Nobel be accused of vanity, so disinterested was he in the trappings of success. On one occasion only did he feel slighted, and that was when the Sankt Gotthard tunnel was inaugurated with much pomp and circumstance in 1882, and Nobel was not invited! He undoubtedly felt that he had, when all was said and done, made a major contribution to the successful completion of the project and was therefore due that little recognition.

Nobel's relations with his family and associates were of an eminently normal nature. He maintained a close relationship with his mother and brothers throughout their lives; he wrote letters, remembered birthdays and was fairly generous with his money. He showed a moving concern for his nieces and nephews, took them to his villa in San Remo and was concerned for their wellbeing. He also had certain social talents and, when the opportunity arose, he knew how to enjoy himself in the circle of his most immediate friends.

But on the whole the millionaire must nevertheless have been lonely. His itinerant lifestyle made conventional bourgeois social relations impossible. He never had a family and lived alone for virtually all his life. He met Bertha Kinsky (later von Suttner) in 1876 and employed her as his secretary. He was clearly enchanted by her, but she left almost immediately to get married.

In the same year, Nobel met a young girl in Vienna, Sofie Hess, whom he took with him to Paris and installed in a flat of

Reconstruction of Nobel's laboratory in San Remo. Photo: Swedish National Museum of Science and Technology.

her own. He wanted her to improve her mind and learn French, but things did not go well. Sofie was chiefly attracted by expensive habits and exclusive clothes, and Alfred's love for her gradually made way for a fatherly concern. He bought her a villa in the Austrian Alps and encouraged her to marry a cavalry officer. In spite of his disappointment, Alfred continued to make Sofie a generous annual allowance. He also bequeathed a sum to her in his will, yet she was not satisfied. She threatened to cause a scandal and only surrendered Alfred's love letters to the executor of his will in return for a considerable sum of money.

Alfred's whirlwind romance had quickly become a burden and he made no further attempts at amorous involvement. Loneliness became a permanent feature of his life.

Alfred Nobel viewed himself with distance, or maybe we

should say with philosophical scepticism. He often described himself as a loner, a hermit, a melancholic or a misanthropist. In one place he wrote: "I am a misanthropist, yet I mean well; I've got a mass of screws loose and am a super idealist who can digest philosophy better than food." It is clear even here that the philanthropist, the humanitarian, or what he chose to call the super idealist, existed side by side with the misanthropist. And it was the idealist in him who drove him to donate his fortune to those who had served mankind through science, literature and work to promote peace.

The Will

THE IDEA of giving away his fortune came by no means out of the blue. Nobel had long pondered the issue; he had even rewritten his will on a number of occasions to try to find the best formulation. One one occasion he had also commented: "In particular I see great inherited wealth as a misfortune which serves only to promote mankind's apathy."

The peace cause was close to Nobel's heart, inspired in part by his contacts with Bertha von Suttner (herself a prizewinner in 1905). Literature fulfilled his intellectual pleasures and science formed the basis of his own work as researcher and inventor. Nobel put his name to the final version of his will on 27th November 1895 at the Swedish-Norwegian Club in Paris.

Alfred Nobel had many homes during the last decades of his life. In 1890, after some problems with the French authorities, he left Paris to set up home in San Remo, Italy. Four years later he bought Bofors ironworks and arms factory in Sweden and set up his Swedish home in the nearby manor house of Björkborn. He installed laboratories in all his homes so that he could continue his experiments. He was clearly homesick for Sweden, but he complained about the country's winter climate. His health began to deteriorate seriously; he visited doctors and health spas with ever greater frequency, yet he never managed to do the most important thing of all, namely "to rest and look after my health", as he himself put it. On 10th December 1896, Alfred Nobel died at his home in San Remo.

Nobel's will took up no more than one side of writing paper. After listing his bequests to relations and other persons who were close to him, Nobel announced that the interest on the whole of the rest of his estate was to be distributed "in the form of prizes to those who, during the preceding year, have conferred the greatest benefit on mankind" in the fields of physics, chemistry, physiology or medicine, literature and work to promote peace. The prizes for physics and chemistry were to be awarded by the Swedish Academy of Sciences; that for physiology or medicine by the Karolinska Institute in Stockholm; that for literature by the Swedish Academy, while the peace laureate was to be chosen by a committee appointed by the parliament of Norway, the country with which Sweden was in union from 1814 until 1905.

By his death, Alfred Nobel had 355 patents registered in his name, and around these he had built up some 90 factories in 20 countries. It is therefore not surprising that the sum of money available to establish the prizes was so great: some 31 million Swedish kronor. The returns were to be used in part for the prizes and in part to augment the capital. By 1st January 1996, the original sum had grown to 2.3 billion Swedish kronor, with the prize money for each of the prizes amounting to 7.4 million Swedish kronor.

The will excited attention around the world. It was not common to donate such large sums of money to scientific and philanthropic causes. Many criticized the international nature of the prizes and felt that they should have been reserved for Swedes. But this would not have suited a cosmopolitan like

SEK 1 (Swedish krona) = GBP 0.10 or USD 0.15

The first Nobel prize ceremony, Stockholm, 10th December 1901. On the podium, Prof. W. K. Röntgen. Photo: © The Nobel Foundation.

Alfred Nobel. Some family members contested the will and a large number of legal and administrative complications had to be settled. This proved a lengthy procedure, but eventually all was resolved and the first Nobel Prizes could be awarded in 1901.

In the years since then the prizes have firmly established themselves as the world's highest civic honours. The announcement of the prizewinners is awaited eagerly each autumn, while the award ceremonies in Stockholm and Oslo on 10 December in the presence of royalty and international dignitaries have become events of great social prestige. The donator himself could hardly have dreamed of the significance that his philanthropy would have for future generations.

Selected Bibliography

Bergengren, Erik, *Alfred Nobel: The Man and His Work*.
    Edinburgh 1962.

Fant, Kenne, *Alfred Nobel*. New York, 1993.

Hellberg, Thomas & Jansson, Lars Magnus, *Alfred Nobel*.
    Stockholm, 1984; new ed. 1986.

*The Nobel Century: An Illustrated History of the Prizes from
    1901 to the Present (1991),* with an introduction by Asa
    Briggs. London, 1991.

Sohlman, Ragnar, *The Legacy of Alfred Nobel: The Story Behind
    the Nobel Prizes*. London 1983.

Tolf, R.W., *The Russian Rockefellers: The Saga of the Nobel
    Family and the Russian Oil Industry*. Stanford, 1976.

Wassoon, T., ed., *Nobel Prize Winners: An H.W. Wilson
    Biographical Dictionary*. New York, 1987.

Alfred Nobel and the Nobel Prizes. Fact Sheets on Sweden,
    FS 15, Swedish Institute, Stockholm.

Published previously
in "Swedish Portraits", a series of
biographies of eminent Swedes:

Emanuel Swedenborg, by Lars
Bergquist, 1986
Olof Palme, by Gunnar Fredriksson,
1986 and 1996
Raoul Wallenberg, by Jan Larsson,
1986 and 1995 (also in German
and Swedish)
Selma Lagerlöf, by Sven Delblanc,
1986 (also in French and German)
Astrid Lindgren, by Vivi Edström,
1987 and 1993 (also in French,
German and Polish)
Vilhelm Moberg, by Gunnar
Eidevall, 1988 and 1996
Fredrika Bremer, by Agneta Pleijel,
1988

Saint Birgitta, by Lars Bergquist,
1991 and 1996
Carl Linnaeus, by Gunnar Broberg,
1992 (also in French)
Ingmar Bergman, by Maaret
Koskinen, 1993 (also in French
and German)
Gustave III, by Erik Lönnroth, 1994
(in French)
August Strindberg, by Björn Meidal,
1995 (also in French and German)
Carl Michael Bellman, by Lars
Huldén, 1995 (also in German,
Russian and Swedish)
Dag Hammarskjöld, by Peter
Wallensteen, 1995 (also in French,
German, Spanish and Swedish)

*Tore Frängsmyr holds a personal professorship in the history of
science at the University of Uppsala, Sweden. He is also director of
a centre for the history of science at the Royal Swedish Academy of
Sciences and editor of 'Les Prix Nobel', the handbook of the Nobel
Foundation. His books include 'Linnaeus, the Man and His Work'
(1983, new edition 1994) and 'Science in Sweden: the Royal
Swedish Academy of Sciences 1739–1989' (1989).*

THE SWEDISH INSTITUTE is a government-financed foundation established to disseminate knowledge abroad about Sweden's social and cultural life, to promote cultural and informational exchange with other countries and to contribute to increased international cooperation in the fields of education and research. The Swedish Institute produces a wide range of publications on many aspects of Swedish society.

In the SWEDEN BOOKSHOP you will find—in several languages—books, brochures, fact sheets and richly illustrated gift books on Sweden, a broad selection of Swedish fiction and children's books, as well as Swedish music, slides, video cassettes and Swedish language courses.

Visit the SWEDEN BOOKSHOP, Sweden House at Hamngatan/Kungsträdgården in Stockholm.

Phone Customer Service: + 46-8-789 20 00

Write to the Swedish Institute,
Box 7434, S-103 91 Stockholm, Sweden
Fax +46-8-20 72 48
e-mail: order @ si.se http://www.si.se.